Robin Lim

Contents

First edition

© LADYBIRD BOOKS LTD MCMLXXXIV

Favourite Poems

chosen by Audrey Daly

Ladybird Books Loughborough

Leisure

What is this life if, full of care,
We have no time to stand and stare.

No time to stand beneath the boughs
And stare as long as sheep or cows.

No time to see, when woods we pass,
Where squirrels hide their nuts in grass.

No time to see, in broad daylight,
Streams full of stars, like skies at night.

No time to turn at Beauty's glance,
And watch her feet, how they can dance.

No time to wait till her mouth can
Enrich that smile her eyes began.

A poor life this if, full of care,
We have no time to stand and stare.

W H Davies

From a Railway Carriage

Faster than fairies, faster than witches,
Bridges and houses, hedges and ditches;
And charging along like troops in a battle
All through the meadows the horses and cattle:
All of the sights of the hill and the plain
Fly as thick as driving rain;
And ever again, in the wink of an eye,
Painted stations whistle by.

Here is a child who clambers and scrambles,
All by himself and gathering brambles;
Here is a tramp who stands and gazes,
And there is the green for stringing the daisies;
Here is a cart run away in the road
Lumping along with man and load;
And here is a mill, and there is a river:
Each a glimpse and gone forever!

Robert Louis Stevenson

The Daffodils

I wandered lonely as a cloud
That floats on high o'er vales and hills,
When all at once I saw a crowd,
A host, of golden daffodils;
Beside the lake, beneath the trees,
Fluttering and dancing in the breeze.

Continuous as the stars that shine
And twinkle on the Milky Way,
They stretched in never-ending line
Along the margin of a bay:
Ten thousand saw I at a glance,
Tossing their heads in sprightly dance.

The waves beside them danced; but they
Out-did the sparkling waves in glee:
A poet could not but be gay
In such a jocund company:
I gazed – and gazed – but little thought
What wealth to me the show had brought:

For oft, when on my couch I lie
In vacant or in pensive mood,
They flash upon that inward eye
Which is the bliss of solitude;
And then my heart with pleasure fills,
And dances with the daffodils.

William Wordsworth

9

Sea-fever

I must go down to the seas again, to the lonely sea
    and the sky,
And all I ask is a tall ship, and a star to steer her by;
And the wheel's kick and the wind's song and the
    white sail's shaking,
And a grey mist on the sea's face, and a grey dawn
    breaking.

I must go down to the seas again, for the call of the
    running tide
Is a wild call and a clear call that may not be denied;
And all I ask is a windy day with the white clouds
    flying,
And the flung spray and the blown spume, and the
    sea-gulls crying.

I must go down to the seas again, to the vagrant
    gypsy life,
To the gull's way and the whale's way where the
    wind's like a whetted knife;
And all I ask is a merry yarn from a laughing
    fellow-rover,
And quiet sleep and a sweet dream when the long
    trick's over.

John Masefield

The Vagabond

Give to me the life I love,
    Let the lave go by me,
Give the jolly heaven above
    And the byway nigh me.
Bed in the bush with stars to see,
    Bread I dip in the river —
There's the life for a man like me,
    There's the life for ever.

Let the blow fall soon or late,
    Let what will be o'er me;
Give the face of earth around
    And the road before me.
Wealth I seek not, hope nor love,
    Nor a friend to know me;
All I seek the heaven above
    And the road below me.

Or let the autumn fall on me
    Where afield I linger,
Silencing the bird on tree,
    Biting the blue finger;
White as meal the frosty field —
    Warm the fireside haven —
Not to autumn will I yield,
    Not to winter even!

Let the blow fall soon or late,
    Let what will be o'er me;
Give the face of earth around,
    And the road before me.
Wealth I ask not, hope nor love,
    Nor a friend to know me;
All I ask the heaven above
    And the road below me.

Robert Louis Stevenson

I Remember,
I Remember

I remember, I remember,
The house where I was born,
The little window where the sun
Came peeping in at morn;
He never came a wink too soon,
Nor brought too long a day,
But now, I often wish the night
Had borne my breath away!

I remember, I remember,
The roses, red and white,
The vi'lets, and the lily-cups,
Those flowers made of light!
The lilacs where the robin built,
And where my brother set
The laburnum on his birthday —
The tree is living yet!

I remember, I remember,
Where I was used to swing.
And thought the air must rush as fresh
To swallows on the wing;
My spirit flew in feathers then,
That is so heavy now,
And summer pools could hardly cool
The fever on my brow!

I remember, I remember,
The fir trees dark and high;
I used to think their slender tops
Were close against the sky:
It was a childish ignorance,
But now 'tis little joy
To know that I'm farther off from heav'n
Than when I was a boy.

Thomas Hood

Macavity: The Mystery Cat

Macavity's a Mystery Cat: he's called the Hidden
    Paw —
For he's the master criminal who can defy the Law.
He's the bafflement of Scotland Yard, the Flying
    Squad's despair:
For when they reach the scene of crime — *Macavity's
    not there!*

Macavity, Macavity, there's no one like Macavity,
He's broken every human law, he breaks the law of
    gravity.
His powers of levitation would make a fakir stare,
And when you reach the scene of crime — *Macavity's
    not there!*
You may seek him in the basement, you may look up
    in the air —
But I tell you once and once again, *Macavity's not
    there!*

Macavity's a ginger cat, he's very tall and thin;
You would know him if you saw him, for his eyes are
     sunken in.
His brow is deeply lined with thought, his head is
     highly domed;
His coat is dusty from neglect, his whiskers are
     uncombed.
He sways his head from side to side, with movements
     like a snake;
And when you think he's half asleep, he's always
     wide awake.

Macavity, Macavity, there's no one like Macavity,
For he's a fiend in feline shape, a monster of
     depravity.
You may meet him in a by-street, you may see him
     in the square —
But when a crime's discovered, then *Macavity's not
     there!*

He's outwardly respectable. (They say he cheats at
  cards.)
And his footprints are not found in any file of
  Scotland Yard's.
And when the larder's looted, or the jewel-case is
  rifled,
Or when the milk is missing, or another Peke's been
  stifled,
Or the greenhouse glass is broken, and the trellis
  past repair −
Ay, there's the wonder of the thing! *Macavity's not
  there!*

And when the Foreign Office find a Treaty's gone
    astray,
Or the Admiralty lose some plans and drawings by
    the way,
There may be a scrap of paper in the hall or on the
    stair —
But it's useless to investigate — *Macavity's not there!*
And when the loss has been disclosed, the Secret
    Service say:
'It *must* have been Macavity!' — but he's a mile
    away.
You'll be sure to find him resting, or a-licking of his
    thumbs,
Or engaged in doing complicated long division sums.

Macavity, Macavity, there's no one like Macavity,
There never was a Cat of such deceitfulness and
    suavity.
He always has an alibi, and one or two to spare:
At whatever time the deed took place — MACAVITY
    WASN'T THERE!
And they say that all the Cats whose wicked deeds
    are widely known
(I might mention Mungojerrie, I might mention
    Griddlebone)
Are nothing more than agents for the Cat who all
    the time
Just controls their operations: the Napoleon of
    Crime!

T S Eliot

The Donkey

When fishes flew and forests walked
    And figs grew upon thorn,
Some moment when the moon was blood
    Then surely I was born.

With monstrous head and sickening cry
    And ears like errant wings,
The devil's walking parody
    On all four-footed things.

Fools! For I also had my hour;
    One far fierce hour and sweet:
There was a shout about my ears,
    And palms before my feet.

G K Chesterton

Cargoes

Quinquireme of Nineveh from distant Ophir,
Rowing home to haven in sunny Palestine,
With a cargo of ivory,
And apes and peacocks,
Sandalwood, cedarwood, and sweet white wine.

Stately Spanish galleon coming from the Isthmus,
Dipping through the Tropics by the palm-green
    shores,
With a cargo of diamonds,
Emeralds, amethysts,
Topazes, and cinnamon, and gold moidores.

Dirty British coaster with a salt-caked smoke stack,
Butting through the Channel in the mad March days,
With a cargo of Tyne coal,
Road-rails, pig-lead,
Firewood, iron-ware, and cheap tin trays.

John Masefield

The Charge of the Light Brigade

Half a league, half a league,
    Half a league onward,
All in the valley of Death
    Rode the six hundred.
'Forward, the Light Brigade!
Charge for the guns!' he said:
Into the valley of Death
    Rode the six hundred.

'Forward, the Light Brigade!'
Was there a man dismay'd?
Not tho' the soldier knew
    Some one had blunder'd:
Theirs not to make reply,
Theirs not to reason why,
Theirs but to do and die:
Into the valley of Death
    Rode the six hundred.

Cannon to right of them,
Cannon to left of them,
Cannon in front of them
    Volley'd and thunder'd;
Storm'd at with shot and shell,
Boldly they rode and well,
Into the jaws of Death,
Into the mouth of Hell
    Rode the six hundred.

Flash'd all their sabres bare,
Flash'd as they turn'd in air,
Sabring the gunners there,
Charging an army, while
    All the world wonder'd:
Plunged in the battery-smoke
Right thro' the line they broke;
Cossack and Russian
Reel'd from the sabre-stroke
    Shatter'd and sunder'd.
Then they rode back, but not,
    Not the six hundred.

Cannon to right of them,
Cannon to left of them,
Cannon behind them
    Volley'd and thunder'd;
Storm'd at with shot and shell,
While horse and hero fell,
They that had fought so well
Came thro' the jaws of Death,
Back from the mouth of Hell,
All that was left of them,
    Left of six hundred.

When can their glory fade?
O the wild charge they made!
    All the world wonder'd.
Honour the charge they made!
Honour the Light Brigade
    Noble six hundred!

Alfred, Lord Tennyson

Clerihews

The Art of Biography
Is different from Geography.
Geography is about Maps,
But Biography is about Chaps.

Sir Christopher Wren
Said, 'I am going to dine with some men.
If anybody calls
Say I am designing St Paul's.'

E C Bentley

A Word of Encouragement

O what a tangled web we weave
When first we practise to deceive!
But when we've practised quite a while
How vastly we improve our style!

J R Pope

There was a young lady named Bright
Whose speed was far faster than light;
    She set out one day
    In a relative way,
And returned home the previous night.

Arthur Buller

After Emerson

Lives of great men all remind us
    As we o'er their pages turn,
That we too may leave behind us
    Letters that we ought to burn.

Anon

The Lake Isle of Innisfree

I will arise and go now, and go to Innisfree,
And a small cabin build there, of clay and wattles
    made:
Nine bean-rows will I have there, a hive for the
    honey-bee,
And live alone in the bee-loud glade.

And I shall have some peace there, for peace comes
    dropping slow,
Dropping from the veils of the morning to where the
    cricket sings;
There midnight's all a glimmer, and noon a purple
    glow,
And evening full of the linnet's wings.

I will arise and go now, for always night and day
I hear lake water lapping with low sounds by the
    shore;
While I stand on the roadway, or on the pavements
    grey,
I hear it in the deep heart's core.

W B Yeats

Casabianca

The boy stood on the burning deck,
    Whence all but he had fled;
The flames that lit the battle's wreck,
    Shone round him o'er the dead.

Yet beautiful and bright he stood,
    As born to rule the storm;
A creature of heroic blood,
    A proud though childlike form.

The flames rolled on; he would not go
    Without his father's word;
That father, faint in death below,
    His voice no longer heard.

He called aloud, 'Say, Father, say,
    If yet my task is done!'
He knew not that the chieftain lay
    Unconscious of his son.

'Speak, Father,' once again he cried,
    'If I may yet be gone!'
— And but the booming shots replied,
    And fast the flames rolled on.

Upon his brow he felt their breath,
    And in his waving hair;
And looked from that lone post of death
    In still yet brave despair;

And shouted but once more aloud,
    'My Father! Must I stay?'
While o'er him fast, through sail and shroud,
    The wreathing fires made way.

They wrapt the ship in splendour wild,
    They caught the flag on high,
And streamed above the gallant child,
    Like banners in the sky.

There came a burst of thunder sound —
    The boy — oh! Where was he?
— Ask of the winds, that far around
    With fragments strewed the sea;

With shroud, and mast, and pennon fair,
    That well had borne their part,
But the noblest thing that perish'd there
    Was that young faithful heart.

Felicia Dorothea Hemans

How Doth
the Little Crocodile

How doth the little crocodile
    Improve his shining tail,
And pour the waters of the Nile
    On every golden scale!

How cheerfully he seems to grin
    How neatly spreads his claws,
And welcomes little fishes in,
    With gently smiling jaws!

Lewis Carroll

The Policeman's Lot

When a felon's not engaged in his employment
    Or maturing his felonious little plans,
His capacity for innocent enjoyment
    Is just as great as any honest man's.
Our feelings we with difficulty smother
    When constabulary duty's to be done:
Ah, take one consideration with another,
    A policeman's lot is not a happy one!

When the enterprising burglar isn't burgling,
    When the cut-throat isn't occupied in crime,
He loves to hear the little brook a-gurgling,
    And listen to the merry village chime.
When the coster's finished jumping on his mother,
    He loves to lie a-basking in the sun:
Ah, take one consideration with another,
    The policeman's lot is not a happy one!

W S Gilbert

31

To Autumn

Season of mists and mellow fruitfulness!
  Close bosom-friend of the maturing sun;
Conspiring with him how to load and bless
  With fruit the vines that round the thatch-eaves
    run;
To bend with apples the moss'd cottage-trees,
  And fill all fruit with ripeness to the core;
    To swell the gourd, and plump the hazel
      shells
  With a sweet kernel; to set budding more
And still more, later flowers for the bees,
Until they think warm days will never cease,
  For Summer has o'er-brimm'd their clammy
    cells.

Who hath not seen thee oft amid thy store?
  Sometimes whoever seeks abroad may find
Thee sitting careless on a granary floor,
  Thy hair soft-lifted by the winnowing wind,
Or on a half-reap'd furrow sound asleep,
  Drowsed with the fume of poppies, while thy
    hook
    Spares the next swath and all its twinèd
      flowers;
And sometimes like a gleaner thou dost keep
  Steady thy laden head across a brook;
  Or by a cider-press, with patient look,
    Thou watchest the last oozings hours by
      hours.

Where are the songs of Spring? Ay, where are they?
    Think not of them, thou hast thy music too, —
While barred clouds bloom the soft-dying day,
    And touch the stubble-plains with rosy hue;
Then in a wailful choir the small gnats mourn
    Among the river sallows, borne aloft
        Or sinking as the light wind lives or dies;
And full-grown lambs loud bleat from hilly bourn;
    Hedge-crickets sing; and now with treble soft
    The redbreast whistles from a garden-croft;
        And gathering swallows twitter in the skies.

John Keats

Who is Silvia?

Who is Silvia? What is she,
That all our swains commend her?
Holy, fair and wise is she;
The heavens such grace did lend her
That she might admired be.

Is she kind as she is fair?
For beauty lives with kindness:
Love doth to her eyes repair,
To help him of his blindness,
And, being help'd, inhabits there.

Then to Silvia let us sing,
That Silvia is excelling;
She excels each mortal thing
Upon the dull earth dwelling:
To her let us garlands bring.

William Shakespeare

The Way of the World

Laugh, and the world laughs with you,
    Weep, and you weep alone;
For the brave old earth must borrow its mirth,
    But has trouble enough of its own.
Sing and the hills will answer,
    Sigh, it is lost on the air;
The echoes rebound to a joyful sound
    And shrink from voicing care.

Rejoice, and men will seek you,
    Grieve, and they turn to go;
They want full measure of your pleasure,
    But they do not want your woe.
Be glad, and your friends are many,
    Be sad, and you lose them all;
There are *none* to decline your nectared wine,
    But *alone* you must drink life's gall.

Feast, and your halls are crowded,
    Fast, and the world goes by.
Forget and forgive – it helps you to live,
    But no man can help you to die;
There's room in the halls of pleasure
    For a long and lordly train,
But one by one, we must all march on
    Through the narrow aisle of pain.

Ella Wheeler Wilcox

If –

If you can keep your head when all about you
    Are losing theirs and blaming it on you,
If you can trust yourself when all men doubt you,
    But make allowance for their doubting too;
If you can wait and not be tired by waiting,
    Or being lied about, don't deal in lies,
Or being hated, don't give way to hating,
    And yet don't look too good, nor talk too wise:

If you can dream – and not make dreams your
      master;
      If you can think – and not make thoughts your
          aim;
If you can meet with Triumph and Disaster
      And treat those two impostors just the same;
If you can bear to hear the truth you've spoken
      Twisted by knaves to make a trap for fools,
Or watch the things you gave your life to, broken,
      And stoop and build 'em up with worn-out tools:

If you can make one heap of all your winnings
      And risk it on one turn of pitch-and-toss,
And lose, and start again at your beginnings
      And never breathe a word about your loss;
If you can force your heart and nerve and sinew
      To serve your turn long after they are gone,
And so hold on when there is nothing in you
      Except the Will which says to them: 'Hold on!'

If you can talk with crowds and keep your virtue,
      Or walk with Kings – nor lose the common
          touch,
If neither foes nor loving friends can hurt you,
      If all men count with you, but none too much;
If you can fill the unforgiving minute
      With sixty seconds' worth of distance run,
Yours is the Earth and everything that's in it,
      And – which is more – you'll be a Man, my son!

Rudyard Kipling

How Doth the Little Busy Bee

How doth the little busy bee
    Improve each shining hour,
And gather honey all the day
    From every opening flower!

How skilfully she builds her cell!
    How neat she spreads the wax!
And labours hard to store it well
    With the sweet food she makes.

In works of labour, or of skill,
    I would be busy too;
For Satan finds some mischief still
    For idle hands to do.

In books, or work, or healthful play,
    Let my first years be passed,
That I may give for every day
    Some good account at last.

Isaac Watts

Night Mail

This is the night mail crossing the Border,
Bringing the cheque and the postal order,

Letters for the rich, letters for the poor,
The shop at the corner and the girl next door.

Pulling up Beattock, a steady climb:
The gradient's against her, but she's on time.

Past cotton grass and moorland boulder
Shovelling white steam over her shoulder,

Snorting noisily as she passes
Silent miles of wind-bent grasses.

Birds turn their heads as she approaches,
Stare from the bushes at her blank-faced coaches.

Sheep dogs cannot turn her course,
They slumber on with paws across.

In the farm she passes no one wakes,
But a jug in the bedroom gently shakes.

Dawn freshens. Her climb is done.
Down towards Glasgow she descends
Towards the steam tugs yelping down the glade of
      cranes,
Towards the fields of apparatus, the furnaces
Set on the dark plain like gigantic chessmen.
All Scotland waits for her:
In the dark glens, beside the pale-green lochs,
Men long for news.

Letters of thanks, letters from banks,
Letters of joy from girl and boy,
Receipted bills and invitations
To inspect new stock or visit relations,
And applications for situations
And timid lovers' declarations
And gossip, gossip from all the nations,
News circumstantial, news financial,
Letters with holiday snaps to enlarge in,
Letters with faces scrawled in the margin,
Letters from uncles, cousins and aunts,
Letters to Scotland from the South of France,
Letters of condolence to Highlands and Lowlands,
Written on paper of every hue,
The pink, the violet, the white and the blue,
The chatty, the catty, the boring, the adoring,
The cold and official and the heart's outpouring,
Clever, stupid, short and long,
The typed and the printed and the spelt all
wrong.

Thousands are still asleep
Dreaming of terrifying monsters,
Or a friendly tea beside the band in Cranston's or
    Crawford's.
Asleep in working Glasgow, asleep in well-set
    Edinburgh,
Asleep in granite Aberdeen.
They continue their dreams;
But shall wake soon and hope for letters,
And none will hear the postman's knock
Without a quickening of the heart,
For who can bear to feel himself forgotten?

W H Auden

Acknowledgments

The compiler and publishers wish to acknowledge
the use of illustrative material as follows:
pages 24/5 and 30/31, Martin Aitchison; 4/5, Roger Bradley;
6/7, 20, and 40/41, Tim Clark; 34, Anne Close; 13, Bruce Coleman Ltd;
16/17, 18/19, Robin Davies; 14/15, Mary Evans Picture Library;
22/3 and 28/9, Frank Humphris; 26/7, The Irish Tourist Board;
43, Ian Morrison; 33, Paul Morrison; 10, The National Maritime Museum;
21, Natural History Photographic Agency; 36, Joan Roy;
8/9 and 39, Harry Stanton; cover, George Towers; 11, Yachting World.

Permission to use copyright poems has been granted as follows:
W H Auden's 'Night Mail' by permission of Faber & Faber,
Publishers, and Random House Inc. Copyright 1938 by W H Auden.
Reprinted from W H Auden's Collected Poems edited by Edward Mendelson;
E C Bentley's 'The Art of Biography' and 'Sir Christopher Wren' from
The Complete Clerihews of E Clerihew Bentley (1981)
by permission of Oxford University Press;
Arthur Buller's 'There was a young lady named Bright'
by permission of Punch; G K Chesterton's 'The Donkey' by permission
of the National Trust and Macmillan Ltd; W H Davies' 'Leisure' by permission
of the Executors of the W H Davies' Estate and Wesleyan University Press;
T S Eliot's 'Macavity: the Mystery Cat' from Old Possum's Book of Practical Cats
copyright 1939 by T S Eliot; renewed 1967 by Esme Valerie Eliot. Reprinted by
permission of Harcourt Brace Jovanovich Inc and Faber & Faber, Publishers;
Rudyard Kipling's 'If' by permission of the National Trust and Macmillan Ltd;
John Masefield's 'Cargoes' and 'Sea-fever' by permission of Macmillan Publishing
Company Inc and the Society of Authors as the literary representative
of the Estate of John Masefield; W B Yeats' 'The Lake Isle of Innisfree'
from Collected Poems of W B Yeats (Macmillan New York 1956)
by permission of Macmillan Publishing Company Inc,
Mr Michael Yeats and Macmillan London Ltd.

Although every effort has been made to trace copyright owners,
this has not always been possible, and we make
apology for any omission.